DIALYSIS IS NOT YOUR LIFE

By: Fred L. Hill

Fred Hill

DIALYSIS IS NOT YOUR LIFE

By: Fred L. Hill

Foreword by Dr. Ari Kramer, MD

Dialysis Is Not Your Life

All quotes are in italics and the author is noted.

ISBN: 9798753956293

Printed in the United States 2021

Published by Reset, Inc.

http://www.dialysisisnotyourlife.com

Dedication

This book is dedicated to my son Haeven "Ace" Hill.

You are my high card. I can always win with you in my life. You are my greatest gift from God. I'm so proud of the young man that you have become. Everything that I've taught you, you've taking it to the next level. Now the teacher has become the student.

I love you with all my heart and everything that I am. You are and have always been my "reason"! Continue to put God 1st, believe in yourself, work hard, and all of your dreams can come true.

Thank you for being my 1st client as a Personal Trainer.

Dad, aka "Papa-doodles."

"May my praises reach the heavens for my Haeven."

Foreword

Some 30 million Americans suffer from kidney disease, which has become the ninth leading cause of death in America. Growing rates of diabetes, hypertension, obesity, and heart disease means nearly 15% of the United States population has chronic kidney disease and 1 in 3 adults are at risk to develop chronic kidney disease.

Many patients feel despair at their loss of health and freedoms and are daunted by the difficult and often painful sacrifices that must be made to remain alive via medical and surgical interventions and operations. They all too often find themselves a part of a healthcare system that can appear both unfeeling and detached of humanity. One that provides life sparing and prolonging therapy yet robs patients of their fundamental dignity of living. A state of affairs that can become so common place that neither patient nor provider any longer recognize this truly sad low state of being that it becomes simply "normal."

When Mr. Hill approached me with this book among his many ideas, I was uncertain to the point of suspicion. His personal request of my time for a non-clinical meeting challenged my comfort with my role as a doctor and his as a patient. It tugged at the edges of my safe well-worn role and practice of medicine - that of being kind, familiar, affable, and available, yet keeping me internally safe and emotionally remote.

I remember well, my feelings of being woken up to the sad status I had allowed myself to fall and becoming alive with the understanding that I had missed the man and merely become familiar with his diagnosis. I had seen his disease, but I had never seen his face, never felt his joys and fears, nor appreciated how much courage he possessed fighting to retain a dignified life.

Shortly after that meeting, this little book found its way to my office desk. Unassuming in size, I again wanted to dismiss it, my short moment of clarity quickly being overwhelmed by my view of safe practical professionalism. And there it sat, a week turned two and three and four. Time and dust settling, my routines well restored. And then, quite unexpectedly, I opened the cover and found myself reading, at first to be through with it, and then because I could not resist. And then again and again because I could not believe the power and inspiration that I drew from it.

I have read and reread this little volume countless times. Each time I am reminded that this book is not about dialysis. It is not a book about disease. It is a book about being human, about perseverance, endurance, and dignity. By weight, it is perhaps one of the greatest, clearest, most inspiring tales of honest passionate living that I have encountered. I encourage you to read it and to share it, the world certainly needs more of it. But before reading,

I give you a fair warning - it will challenge you to change your life and to be better. It will warm your heart and you will want to fight like hell to live fully. Best of life and living to you all,

Ari Kramer, MD
Chairman Vascular Access
Spartanburg Regional Medical Center

Comments About D.I.N.Y.L.

Ari Kramer, MD
Chairman Vascular Access
Spartanburg Regional Medical Center
"But before reading, I give you a fair warning - it will challenge you to change your life and to be better. It will warm your heart and you will want to fight like hell to live fully."

Dr. Ingemar Davidson MD, PhD
Transplant and access surgeon
"At Kidney Academy, a forum for the clinical team who manage dialysis access patients, we believe that the patient should be at the center of decision making throughout the treatment pathway, and we value Fred sharing his personal story to share hope with other patients undergoing a similar experience."

Therese Wykoff, MS
Program Director, Kidney Academy

"Fred shares a real-life account of his journey dealing with kidney disease. There are many ups and downs through this process, and he stresses that as a patient you must educate yourself and be the captain of your own ship as you navigate this path."

Dori Schatell, MS
Executive Director
Medical Education Institute, Inc

"I enjoyed your book and agree 100% about the importance of attitude and motivation. I know a LOT of folks who could really use your messages. Thank you for doing what you do!"

Dr. Murdock's M.D.
Nephrologist

"I have had the privilege to care for Fred Hill. I am privileged to be a part of his journey and am excited to see what his future holds. As a physician caring for those patients with renal disease many times is hard to help a patient really understand CKD. So many complex things that occur with the stages of kidney disease and the complexity of medical treatment makes it hard

to realize the intellectual, psychological, and physical, changes a patient must deal with. This book will help my practice and many other nephrologist practices get down on a level that will help patients deal with CKD and ESRD."
"Thank you for your hard work. This book will be used extensively."

Frances Wise RN, BSN, MN, ACNP
"This awesome book is a culmination of many hard-long hours to put it all together. It touches my heart as a caregiver to really try to understand the impact of dialysis on a patient's life. I get so wrapped up in the mechanisms of treating the patient that it is hard to really understand the impact."

"This book will widely be used to help my patients deal with many emotional, physical, and intellectual changes all living with dialysis. It will help them work collectively with me to give them the best care."

Acknowledgements

I would like to thank God for the opportunity to create an exercise/wellness program to help people with kidney disease to know they can still live their best lives.

I would like to say thank you to the unknown family that made the decision to gift me with the kidney of their loved one. Your sacrifice gave me another chance at life without being on dialysis.

My wife (Phyllis Hill), thank you for your sacrifice of helping me at every stage of this journey and challenging me to be better. I love you Babydoll!!!My son (Haeven Hill), I could not have made it through these hard times without you. You are the calm in the storm. I Love you man!!!

To my father Jerry Hill Sr. You were my 1st client for Better Health Fitness & Motivation. Thank you for always being there for me. I love you Pop!!!

Frances Hill, I love you. I always feel safe with you, as a son should. Thank you for your love, prayers, and wise counsel.

Pastor Renee Glen, thank you for covering me and my family. I am grateful for you loving me through my good and my bad. I love you.

To my brothers Jerry “Bugg” Hill, Rexx Hill, Terance “Tee” Jackson, and my sister Candace Cathcart, thank you for your support and encouragement.

Warren James Sr. you were there for me like a true brother. I will always be grateful for who you are in my life.

Patrice James, thank you for proof reading and all of your great ideas to help make this book what it is. You are awesome!

TJ Watson, thank you for the book cover. You never fail to come through whenever I need you.

Dr. Ari Kramer MD, thank you for taking to time to listen to my thoughts and ideas in the creation of Better Health Fitness & Motivation and Dialysis Is Not Your Life. Thank you for believing in me and all the people and opportunities you introduced to me.

Frances Wise RN, BSN, MN, ACNP, thank you for believing in me, supporting me and all your help. Thank you for helping this vision to come true.

Dr. Bruce Murdock MD (my Nephrologists), thank you for being straight with me all these years.

Pam Glenn (my 1st nurse) and all the staff at Foothills Nephrology, thank you for taking care of me.

Kenneth Jackson, thank you for being my 1st client with Better Health Fitness & Motivation and always supporting and encouraging me.

Ameer Natson, my mentor, coach, friend, and brother. Thank you for showing up on time and revealing a greater side of life. "This is only the beginning. We're going all the way!"

Dr. Ingemar Davidson MD, PhD, Therese Wykoff MS and the Kidney Academy, thank you for your support and every opportunity you have given me.

Dori Schatell MS, thank you for you for proof reading and corrections to the book.

Preface

Many people who are on dialysis are living beneath the privilege of enjoying life. Many of the things in life that once brought joy and satisfaction are no longer priorities. Dialysis is hard on the body and the mind. It causes physical aches, pains, and changes in the body. It robs you of your energy and strength. It can steal your confidence and cause a negative impact on your life.

Being on dialysis not only affects you, but also your spouse, children, family and friends. Everyone is going through what you are experiencing. Everyone is on an emotional rollercoaster. Everyone is asking why? Everyone is wondering about the future because of the horror stories they have heard.

Even though some of the stories may be true, it does not mean that your life will be another scene in the next chapter of the dialysis horror stories. You can choose not to focus on the negative things that you've heard. Your experience on dialysis is all up to you.

You must decide to *live* while on dialysis and not just exist on dialysis. Dialysis is a lifeline. It is not your life. Dialysis does not have you. You have dialysis. ***You have more control while on dialysis than you think.***

When dialysis has you, you are controlled by dialysis. People who are controlled by dialysis go to the clinic 3 times a week for 4 plus hours each run. When they get home from dialysis, they eat and rest. Sadly, it is the same eat and rest cycle on the days off in-between dialysis. This cycle is causing your body to deteriorate and gives the excuse: "I'm tired because I'm on dialysis."

People who are controlled by dialysis wait on the doctor to tell them what is wrong or what they need to do for better dialysis runs and better lab readings. The ignorance of not knowing your body can cause you to always remain in the doctor's office or in the emergency room.

People who are controlled by dialysis make life decisions in fear of dialysis. "What if? What about this? I'm afraid because of…" which causes them to end up missing out on enjoying life.

To take control of your life on dialysis, you must change your perspective. You ***can*** live a quality level of life while on dialysis, but you must decide not to allow it to control your life. Tell yourself, "Dialysis is not my life."

This book will include a personal account of my experiences on dialysis from the beginning. As you read, you may relate to the different stages of dialysis which may or may not be similar to your own personal journey. This book is aimed to help you control your response to being on dialysis and give you the courage to get your life back. Just because you are on dialysis does not mean you should allow it to control your life!

Contents

Chapter 1

"The Diagnosis"

"Never be ashamed of your story. Someone needs to hear it."**-** Fred Hill

In early 2000, I was diagnosed with Polycystic Kidney Disease. PKD is a hereditary condition where cysts grow on your kidneys and slowly cause them to fail. In December of 2011, I was told to make a choice to begin dialysis treatments.

One option was to begin hemodialysis. This is where a fistula (an artery linked to a vein) is created in the arm or leg by a surgeon. You are placed on machine for four hours to clean the blood, three non-consecutive days a week. The other option was peritoneal dialysis **(PD)**, where a catheter is placed in the abdomen to allow fluid to be placed into the peritoneal lining of the abdomen in 2hr – 4hr increments for 24hrs to clean the blood.

On February 9th, 2012, I started PD. I was terrified, because my grandmother, aunt, sister, and cousin all had polycystic kidney disease and they all died. Now I had been diagnosed with the same disease on the same machines and facing the same fate. It felt like I was looking down the barrel of a loaded gun and waiting for a bullet with my name on it to take me out of this world.

All I could think was I'm going to die, and I'm not ready. I was forty years old and there was so much I still hadn't accomplished. My life was over. There would be no more time with my wife and son. My wife was going to be a widow and my son was going to grow up without a father. My father was going to bury another child and my brothers and sister were going to lose another sibling. They all were going to watch me wither away and die. This was out of my control.

When you can't control what is happening, you must decide to control the way you respond to what is happening. **That is where your power is.**

I couldn't control being on dialysis, but I could control my response. Dialysis did not have me; I had dialysis, and I was determined it would ***not*** control my life. The negative thinking of all that I would leave behind in death became the drive for me to live.

Chapter 2

"The Grieving Process"

"Turn the pain into power"- T.D. Jakes

Grief is mostly linked with death, but grief is the normal process of reacting to any type of loss. The loss can be physical (death), social (divorce), or occupational (job). Being on dialysis causes grief because of the physical loss of kidney function (renal failure) which can lead to a spiral of loss in your life.

Renal failure can cause loss in bone density, muscle mass, muscle strength and energy. These losses can lead to depression, anxiety, low sex drive, loss of erections, low self-esteem due to body image, joint pain, and walking imbalance—just to name a few. It can strip you of your confidence and cause a negative impact on your quality of life.

Now, negative reactions to these spirals of losses can lead to divorce, occupational, and relational losses. That's why it is important to deal with the grief of being on dialysis. You must go through the process of grief and not get stuck living in the emotions of anger, guilt, anxiety, sadness, and despair. Living in your emotions can make you bitter and mean or sad and depressed. Neither is good for your life.

We all have a reason or reasons to get stuck in grief and live our lives through our emotions, denial, anger, depression, or whatever negative emotion we may feel.

Yet, it is not fair to you or the people around you to live your life stuck in grief. When you are stuck in grief you tend to treat the people around you according to the emotional slump you're in at that moment. You treat others like they are the reason for your grief. After receiving this diagnosis, I found myself going through different stages of the grieving process.

Denial:

When I was told that I had to make the decision to go on dialysis, I was in denial because I felt that I didn't have any symptoms of renal failure. I knew my BUN and Creatinine numbers were far above normal, but I didn't feel sick, and I wasn't retaining water.

I ultimately decided to go to my family doctor for a second opinion. He said that I should have already been on dialysis. My numbers were so high that my body was at the point of being uremic and could experience brain damage.

I still didn't believe it until one day at work, I became so dizzy that I couldn't see straight. My head was swimming, and it wouldn't go away. I had to accept that I needed to go on dialysis.

Anger:

After going on dialysis, I became angry because I didn't understand *why me*. I was helpless with no answers, and I couldn't fix it. I didn't ask for PKD. I didn't drink or smoke. I exercised five days a week. I went to church. I was a good person. How could God let this happen to me?

I was so angry, and I didn't know how to direct my anger. I didn't know who to be mad at. I didn't like the changes in my life that I had to make to accommodate being on dialysis. I didn't like being identified as sick. I tried to think of who I could blame, but there was no one. I tried to figure a way to get my life back and I couldn't. I was trapped.

Several things ran through my mind, "Is it going to be like this forever? Am I going to die like my grandmother, aunt, cousin, and sister? Will my wife still want me and see me as a man or as a sick burden? How will my son see me now? I feel like I'm losing a grip on my life. Who am I? I'm lost without direction. I'm just here and I hate it. I'm feeling sorry for myself. I'm depressed."

Depression:

Without even recognizing it, I went from feeling angry to being depressed. Depression sucks. It blinds you of everything good and beautiful. You don't notice the people around you and you become nonchalant to everything happening in your surroundings.

It cripples you from moving forward. You only respond to what reminds you of being on dialysis and how it makes your life so bad. This was the hardest place for me to be in. I felt like it would never get better, and nothing would ever change because I was sick and on dialysis.

You respond by crying when you see people in good health, crying when you see parents playing with their kids, crying when you hear of couples enjoying their date night, crying when you hear or see anyone enjoying life.

It all reminds you that you are on dialysis, and you can no longer enjoy life the way you once did. You find yourself whining about the people, places, and moments you missed or took for granted. It becomes an aimless, twenty-four hours a day, seven days a week, selfish cycle of emptiness.

Acceptance:

Finally, I accepted the fact that I was a peritoneal dialysis patient. I had a PD catheter hanging out of my belly. I had to perform the fluid exchanges 7 days a week to remain alive.

I accepted that dialysis was a part of my life but, it was not my life.

It took over a year to get to this point, but I made it. It was the best thing for me because I realized that dialysis was not a punishment for me, but it was actually keeping me alive, and I became grateful for being on dialysis because it was the reason I wasn't dead. I became grateful for my Nephrologists, the PD nurses, and my dietitian. I was grateful for the support system from my wife, son, and family.

I finally saw it. I wasn't dead. So, why was I living my life lifeless? It was because I was stuck living my life in grief. I was stuck living in anger and depression because I didn't think I deserved this life sentence on dialysis. I was innocent. I did nothing to be in this predicament.

Now, the question became, "How was I going to live a quality level of life on dialysis?" I didn't know the answer then, but I was determined to find it.

Seeking help:

I can sympathize with people stuck in grief because I've been there. You're going to go through grief but others do not deserve to be treated badly because of your affliction. You must seek the help that you need whether it is through therapy, family counseling, spiritual counseling or help centers to get to the place of accepting your new normal so you can live.

Being stuck living in grief was hard, but when I accepted dialysis and realized I wasn't dead, I chose to live and have a better quality of life while I was on dialysis. I had to love myself again with the PD catheter in my belly and everything else that came with being on dialysis. I had to get my confidence back, my sexy back, my happiness and lifestyle back.

Getting up:

The first thing I had to do was get up. I had to tell myself daily to get up because life was more than just waiting on the next dialysis treatment. It was more than being angry or feeling sorry for myself. I had been given an opportunity to live through the assistance of dialysis. Now the question became, "What was I going to do with my new opportunity to live?"

There is an opportunity for you to live a quality level of life while on dialysis. Make the decision today to live life out loud. Live your life big. Go for your dreams. Remember that **You have dialysis. Dialysis does not have you.**

Chapter 3

"The New Normal"

"It's your decisions and not your conditions that determine your destiny"- Tony Robbins

When I started dialysis, my nephrologists said I must learn to know my body. I was like, "I'm forty years old and if I don't know my body by now, I'll never know it." However, he was meaning, I was now on dialysis and the machine was removing the toxins from my body. Therefore, my body was going to go through some changes, and I had to know what my body was telling me. I had to face the fact that life as I once knew it no longer existed.

Being aware of your body:

Every patient is different and may or may not have the same experience.

I had pains that I never had before. I had spells where all of a sudden I didn't feel good. There were times I became so hungry that I felt like I was going to vomit. Some days I was extremely tired. Other days I couldn't sleep.

Knowing your body will give you the answers to symptoms like these. You will gain knowledge as you pay attention to your body and learn from your nephrologists, nurse, and dietitian.

Pay attention to your hair, skin, dialysis exit site, tingling in your hands and feet, and swelling in your legs and ankles. Notice how you feel before and after each dialysis treatment, taking medication, and even eating certain foods. There will also be other things you learn to know about your body that will build your confidence to thrive on dialysis.

Knowing your body means asking every question you may have to your nephrologists, nurse, and dietitian. They are here to help you get the knowledge you need to succeed on dialysis. Knowledge is power. You will gain the knowledge to know that they are here to serve you by showing and teaching you things that are necessary for your body, mind, and spirit to be healthy and remain healthy.

Knowing your body makes you proactive. Being proactive gives you the ability to control your reaction to the situation by staying ahead of many issues that derive from being on dialysis rather than responding to them after they have happened. Always responding after the fact can be dangerous. Some patients have waited too late before responding to issues and it didn't work out well.

Don't wait until you get a blood infection before responding. Do what is necessary ***not*** to get an infection. Be proactive. It is detrimental

not to become sick with a cold, flu, or pneumonia. Do what is necessary to ensure your blood test results are within normal specifications.

Take precautions to ensure your fistula/graft or PD catheter are protected so they will last as long as possible. Make sure any doctor's notes, new meds, extra or fewer doses are discussed each day before starting your dialysis treatment.

Being open:

You must learn to tell your Nephrologists everything and I mean everything, no matter how hard or embarrassing it may be. I promise you there is nothing you can say that they haven't already heard, and they have the answers you need to comfort your fear and distress. They will give you the knowledge and tools you need to proactively respond to life on dialysis.

Watching your diet:

The reason for dialysis is to remove waste from the blood. The waste build-up is mainly from the foods we eat. Your eating habits can be a matter life or death. What you eat or not eat can affect the phosphorous, potassium, sodium, glucose, calcium, and fluid levels in your body. Too much of some or too less of another can be fatal.

It is important that you listen to your dietitian and follow the diet plan that is designed for you. Know the importance and results of everything on the monthly lab reports. Keeping your blood levels in normal range makes a great difference in how you feel.

Fighting off illnesses:

How you feel determines your quality of life. Dialysis makes your immune system weak, so it is hard to fight off illnesses. Therefore, stay aware of your surroundings. Pay attention to who is sick around you and be aware of the flu and pneumonia seasons. Your nephrologist will offer the shots as a precaution.

Don't be ashamed to wear a face mask as a safeguard because germs are everywhere. Make sure your exit sites remain clean and frequently wash your hands. What may be simple germs to a normal person may become fatal for you. I'm not saying this to make you a germophobic. I only want you to feel good, take your health seriously, and live a quality level of life.

What works for you:

Know what works for you. This takes time because you are learning your body all over again. For instance, I never needed antacids until starting dialysis. On (PD), I ate in between exchanges instead of eating while I had fluid in my belly.

I used prescription eye drops on the PD catheter exit site to prevent an infection. I taped plastic over the PD catheter when showering to prevent the catheter from pulling and dangling. I arranged the fluid bags to make my daily exchanges easier. You will figure out what works for you as you continue on dialysis.

Another way to know your body is to ask other people about their experiences on dialysis. When I was on hemodialysis (HD), the people didn't talk much. It was, "Good morning and see you next time," but if I asked a question, they were nice enough to answer.

My first day scheduled to start HD, I was terrified. I didn't know what to expect. They told me to just relax, watch television, and wait out the four hours. They told me about the strange feeling of the blood coming out and going back into my body. They warned me about the itching extremely dry skin and the best moisturizing lotions to prevent chapping, cracking, and chafing.

The nurses recommended eating before and/or after the HD treatment. The blood is being cleansed, so eating during the treatment is defeating the purpose. They also recommended rotating the needle insertions for treatment. It may hurt but it helps prevent deformities in the fistula /graft and causes it to last longer.

Learn how to respond to the issues of dialysis and not react. Build trust between you and your doctor, nurses, and dietitian. ***Remember, no one knows you better than you***. Keep it that way, even while on dialysis.

Chapter 4

"M.O.V.E."

"If you can't fly, run. If you can't run, walk. If you can't walk, crawl. But by all means keep moving."- Dr. Martin Luther King

"Healthy self," broken down is "heal-thy-self." It is extremely important to do ***your*** part to better your health. Dialysis does its job to help clean the blood, but at the same time, your bones are getting weaker. Your body is retaining more fluid, and your muscles are losing mass and strength which causes you to be weaker and have little energy. It is your job to build your body to enjoy life. You must become more active. You have to "M.O.V.E." (Maximize, Overcome, Visualize, Execute).

Maximize - Learn to see yourself greater than your renal failure condition. Take advantage of every opportunity that presents itself. Develop a drive to be strong, confident, important, and healthy, to be your best you.

Overcome – Overcome your fear of dialysis. Strengthen your mind and body to defeat the struggles of being on dialysis so you will understand that dialysis is not a weakness; it is a strength.

Visualize – Envision yourself living a quality level of life. See yourself accomplishing all your goals, hopes and dreams. Focus on the positive in every area of your life.

Execute – Be enthusiastic about life. Become active in body and lively in spirit. Create and work the plan to achieve all you have visualized to make the best of your life for yourself and those you love and care about.

Becoming Active:

Dialysis will cause changes in your body and in your life, but you can decide the magnitude of the changes. The choice is up to you. There are many people on dialysis who are inactive. ***Being inactive will lead to numerous medical issues.***

When I began dialysis, there were things I could no longer do, so I learned to modify. I couldn't swim or play contact sports with my son, but I ***could*** throw a football and practice plays and Running Back routes with him. I could ride bikes, shoot basketball, and exercise daily.

Remaining active allowed me to maintain a good weight. I had more energy, muscle mass and strength. In time, I became more confident and no longer depressed. Eventually, I regained a love for life.

You may not be into fitness, but that is not an excuse. Cardiovascular exercise is great for your heart and can help you lose weight, tone your body, and improve your overall health. You can join a gym, work in your garden, walk the neighborhood or play with your children or grandkids. ***Just do something!***

You may not do much on your assigned HD day but get active on your days off. Patients on PD can do something every day. Before you start an exercise program, check with your nephrologist. He or she can prescribe physical therapy if you need it.

Living your life:

It's your life to live. Don't allow the fear of being on dialysis rob you of your health and living your life. Don't let fear decide your future. Stop being afraid of what could go wrong and start being confident about what could go right.

Every day is not going to be easy but don't let a bad day make you feel as if you have a bad life. M.O.V.E. and change the quality of life you're living. You may never have perfect health due to renal failure, but you can have better health.

"It's never too late to change your life!!!"- Fred Hill

Chapter 5

"Motivation Is Key"

"Life is a matter of choices and every choice you make makes you."- John C. Maxwell

You need to find your motivation to be proactive and in control of your responses on dialysis because every day is not going to be a great day. There will be some hard days and some sleepless nights. You may have some pain in your body and some confusing times, but you are in charge of how you respond. You must motivate yourself to M.O.V.E.

Motivation is more than a bunch of quotes. Remember, quotes will not work unless you do the work. You've got to do the work. John C. Maxwell said, ***"Life is a matter of choices and every choice you make makes you."***

You must get up every morning and tell yourself, ***"I can do this"***, because you really can. Motivation begins with you believing in yourself and sorting out what matters to you. What are your reasons for wanting to go on?

In other words, what is your why? Your "***why***" is your center. It is your push to keep going when you want to give up. It is what resets your focus when life has distracted you from being able to M.O.V.E.

It is good to have a support system of people surrounding you, but if you don't believe in yourself, then what's the purpose? You have got to be the one who wants change in your life. Sometimes it is going to be a challenge motivating yourself. During those times, revert to your "***why.***"

My "why," was I ***didn't*** want to die on dialysis like my relatives. I wanted to live a quality life on dialysis, and I wanted to receive a kidney transplant. I had to focus to break the habits of fear that kept me in the dialysis survival mode and create new habits that would become relevant in thriving and living a purposed-driven life while on dialysis. I was determined to make my life meaningful to me, and all those around me.

Doing the work:

Change first starts from within your mind. ***Your desire to change must be greater than your desire to stay the same.*** You need to want your "why" more than you are afraid of the change it will take to get it. If you change nothing, nothing will change. In other words, don't expect to see a change if you don't make one. Push yourself to do what needs to be done in your life without influence from other people.

YOU are the one on dialysis. **YOU** are the one with a fistula / graft or catheter in your body. It's your body and **YOU** are the one who is going to have to motivate yourself.

You must love and value yourself. Going on dialysis can make you feel different about yourself and cause you not to value yourself. Your value as a person does not decrease based on the circumstances of your life. Your circumstance has changed, not your value. You are still important, effective, desirable, appreciated, and worth your weight in gold. Therefore, don't allow that to be taken away because of dialysis.

Don't settle for the mundane life on dialysis. Make the changes to be the above average person on dialysis. Stay motivated!

No excuses:

***"Action is the foundational key to all success."*- Pablo Picasso**

No excuses! Excuses don't help or bring you closer to your goals of a better life. Rather than making excuses for why you can't get it done, focus on all the reasons why you must make it happen. If it is important to you, you will find a way. When you lose all of your excuses, you will find your results. ***"Decide, commit, succeed." "Be stronger than your excuse"***- Nike Slogan

Avoid Making Comparisons:

On this quest to better health and a better life, beware of comparing yourself to others. It's easy to look at people who have no health problems and compare yourself to them. It is also easy to look at other dialysis patients who are in worse shape than you and compare yourself to them. This can be dangerous because it can produce negative thoughts.

Comparing yourself to healthy people causes you to focus on your illness and become depressed by your current situation, wishing things were like they were before renal failure. This will make it hard for you to accept your present status and prevent you from expecting a better life in the future.

Comparing yourself to dialysis patients in a worse condition than you can cause you to feel guilty for living well while on dialysis. I remember when I went to the Medical University of South Carolina (MUSC) in Charleston, South Carolina for blood work and testing to qualify for the kidney transplant list.

I walked into a room with other people who wanted and needed kidney, liver, and/ or pancreas transplants. I immediately began to feel bad because a lot of people in the room seem to need a transplant more than I did. I was doing well and had plans to live life with a new kidney, but others appeared to be at the point of death if they didn't get a kidney transplant and I didn't think it was fair for me to get a transplant before they did.

I told my doctor how I felt, and she said, "*It's not your fault that you are doing well, and others are not.*" I didn't know what they were or were not doing while on dialysis that was causing their condition to be worse. So, do not feel sorry or apologize for doing good while on dialysis. Doing well ***should*** be rewarded with the opportunity to receive a kidney transplant.

That is why you must continue to do well and be the example to other patients so that they, too, can have dialysis and not let dialysis have them. Your only comparison is the person you see in the mirror. Each day make the comparison to yourself to ensure that you are better than the person you saw in the mirror yesterday.

Chapter 6

"Living vs. Existing"

"The purpose of life, after all, is to live it, to taste experience to the utmost, to reach out eagerly and without fear for newer and richer experience."- Eleanor Roosevelt

There is a difference between living and existing. ***Existing is surviving.*** It is accepting whatever life brings to you but lacking the will to change for the better. ***Living is thriving***. ***Living is winning***.

Being better than you were yesterday is a win. Putting forth the effort to change your life for the better can be a win. Making progress toward your goals is a win and winning is living. Only you can define your win for your life. So, live to be better in every area of your life so you may enjoy a life of winning while on dialysis.

Living your life:

Many people on dialysis are alive but not living. The fear of what might happen to cause their lives to worsen has robbed them of living. Never let fear decide your future. You only have one life to live, so live it. Regardless of "whatever," decide to live your life. Life comes to those who still hope after disappointment, who still believe after calamity, and who refuse to give up.

No matter who you are or how long you've been on dialysis, ***you can change your life now***. Nothing changes if nothing changes. Your life will not get better by chance. It gets better by change. Change can be scary but rewarding.

Everything you want in life is on the other side of fear. Fear causes doubt and excuses. The "What if syndrome" comes from fear. What if something bad happens? What if something happens to my fistula? What if this? What if that?

Don't become a prisoner of your own excuses. Don't let the fear of what could happen make nothing happen. Stop being afraid of what could go wrong and start being positive about what could go right. Believe that living is the only option.

The secret of change is to focus all of your energy not on fighting the old, but on building the new.

Living is a decision. You are one decision away from a totally different life. My decision to live changed my life. It was scary in the beginning, because I didn't have a guide to teach me how. I lived in the fear of, "what not to do" but I wanted the knowledge of what I could do. I slowly figured out what worked for me and gained the experience of knowing that dialysis was not my life.

I found out how to exercise to get my energy level up. I went on vacations to the beach, went on a cruise. I went dancing. I continued to train my son in football. I decided not to be a victim on dialysis but to live my life.

Deciding to live is exciting: you smile more, dream big, laugh out loud, and realize how blessed you are for taking the advantage of being alive. Deciding to live while on dialysis is going to be challenging but if it doesn't challenge you, it won't change you.

Life will always put obstacles in your way. You will never be in the perfect condition to achieve your desires, but it is up to you to take control, and make the choices that bring change in your life to get what you desire.

Desire to live a quality level of life on dialysis. Don't allow your renal situation to control your mind, feelings, and emotions. Live in and for today. Whatever happened yesterday, find a way to let it go. You can't reach for anything new if your hands are full of yesterday's disappointments. Tell yourself, ***"Today will be better than yesterday, and I have the power to make it so."***

Get back to the things that used to make you happy. Break the dialysis routine. Don't get stuck in the dialysis/fluid exchange and then do-nothing rut. Get back to health. Take care of you. Exercise and eat better. Get your energy level up. Regain your confidence. Love yourself and your life.

Create goals to spend quality time with your spouse, children, and family. Set life goals (weight-loss, vacations, books, and hobbies, etc.) whatever makes you happy. Start living and not just existing. Gain control of your everyday living.

To gain control of your everyday living, you must first gain control over your health. Better health equals a better life. Live healthy and smart to prevent common sicknesses and infections.

Exercise and stretch to improve cardiovascular, muscle health and arthritis/joint pain. Stay positive and gravitate toward personal things of interest.

After going on dialysis, I had to ***learn*** to love life again. I had to create a lifestyle of balanced living with having fun. I learned to make the best of each day by being positive and living each day to the fullest. I focused on one day at a time and found my life again.

Being positive:

Surround yourself with positivity. Dialysis is not easy and to place yourself in negative situations or have negative people around you is not the answer. It is up to you to remove yourself from negativity. If something or someone is not helping you gain knowledge or get better, it is a waste of time and time is not meant to be wasted.

Time should be purposed in providing what is essential for your life. That is why positivity is so important. Positive people produce positive thoughts. When you control what you think, you can control what you do.

Positive thinking produces positive results. When you control your thinking to be positive, you can visualize accomplishing your goals. You will have a clear visual definition of your personal success. When you can envision yourself reaching and completing your goals, you will begin to believe that it is really possible, because seeing is believing.

In the beginning, being positive was hard because of those in my family who died on dialysis with the same PKD that I had. I knew that thinking about death and waiting to die was not the answer. So, I had to change my thinking from negative to positive because I wanted to live.

I removed myself from people who were feeling sorry for me and talking as if my life was over. I drew closer to the people and activities that made me feel alive. ***I set goals for myself*** to get in shape, so I could be more active and not look or act like a dialysis patient.

I continued to date my wife and be active in my son's life. I remained spiritual to keep my faith and peace of mind. I was determined not to allow dialysis to take away my purpose in life and I believed it was possible.

"Small disciplines repeated with consistency everyday lead to great achievements gained slowly over time."- John Maxwell

Believing in yourself is essential to staying motivated. To succeed in anything, you first must believe that you can. Your only limit is you. Believing in yourself gives you the confidence and determination to achieve what dialysis makes you think is impossible.

Focus on staying dedicated to the process of creating a better quality of life while on dialysis. It's not always going to be easy, and it will not happen overnight but if you continue to

M.O.V.E., your life is going to change for the better.

"As one goes through life one learns that if you don't paddle your own canoe, you don't move."- Katherine Hepburn

It sounds hard and heartless, but it is the truth. You've got to get up every single day and tell yourself, "M.O.V.E." Remind yourself that dialysis is not your life. No one else can do it for you. The struggle may not always get easier, but you can become stronger than the struggle physically, mentally, emotionally, and spiritually.

"It's the repetition of affirmations that lead to belief. And once that belief becomes a deep conviction, things begin to happen."-Muhammad Ali

In the book, "*The Little Engine That Could*," the little engine started out saying, ***"I think I can,"*** and the more he said it, the more he believed it. When he believed he could do it, he accomplished what he hoped to. Motivating yourself starts in the mind. You must first think change in your mind, and then you can change it in your life. You are the captain of your ship. You have the power to change the destination of your life on dialysis.

As you M.O.V.E. towards a better quality of life, be patient and recognize your positive efforts, because it takes time before you see results. Life change is not going to happen overnight, so remain composed and persistent in your daily effort. Positive efforts every day bring you closer to achieving your goals.

You do not have to wait until you reach your goal to be proud of yourself. Be proud of each step you take toward your goals and celebrate your progress. A little progress is better than no progress, and no matter how slow your progress, you are ahead of all those who are not trying at all. Learn to enjoy the journey to a better life and a better you.

Every day is not going to be the same. You will have good and bad days, and it is up to you to make the good days outweigh the bad. Stay focused on one day at a time. Set daily goals and stick to a routine to make sure you complete your goals.

Stick to a routine to create a planned system of consistency and discipline to yield results. Your consistency and discipline will dictate your success and make it harder for you to quit. Consistency gives you the confidence and determination to take control of being a dialysis patient and live a quality level of life.

Live intentional:

I make a conscious effort daily to live each day better than the day before. I plan my day the night before to intentionally live my life and accomplish goals. I have written my dreams and personal life goals in journals and consistently work toward bringing them to life. Dialysis has given me another chance at life, and I deliberately live my life with purpose. I plan to make a positive impact with everyone in my life and those I meet along the way.

I have made plans to do things I've never done before like see the world, make love on an airplane, ride a camel, drive a race car, jump out of a plane just to name a few. Now, what about you?

What are ***your*** dreams and aspirations? What are your expectations in life? Now is the time to plan and make a conscious effort to see them come to fruition. Do not allow dialysis to cause your life to stop or your dreams to die. The power is in your hands to intentionally make it happen.

Live your life out loud! Live and enjoy your life. You only have one life to live and you must tell yourself, ***"I'll be damned to allow dialysis to suck the life out of me. I will not be miserable another day. I will live my life on purpose out loud for everyone to see."***

You are on dialysis. Dialysis does not control your life. It gives you an opportunity to live. So, take this chance that dialysis has given you, seize the moment to take hold of your life and live your best life without regrets.

Chapter 7

“The Power to Reset”

“You have the power to reset your life at any given moment.”-Fred Hill

The power to reset is creating a positive mindset to win in every aspect of life through self-love and faith. Self-love is not selfish love. Selfish love is a love only for yourself. Everything is about you and your mindset is that everything revolves around you.

Self-love is a love to ***better*** yourself, not only for yourself but also for everyone connected to you in life. It is a love for yourself to become the best you for you, your spouse, your children, your family, your dreams, your business, and anything or anyone that is important to you in your life.

Having the power to reset gives you the ability to take ownership of your life. Therefore, you no longer point the finger to blame others for what is wrong in your life. Having the mindset to reset gives you the power and permission to change your mind. When you change your mind, you change your mental perspective to see things capable of being achieved. When you change your outlook and see all that you desire can be accomplished, you change your life.

The power to reset is a decision. Whatever you are not changing, you are choosing. So, develop a mindset that aligns with the life you truly want to live and go get it. The power to reset is **work!** Nothing is going to be handed to you and there are no promises that living on dialysis is going to be easy, but it can be better if you are willing to put in the work to reset your mind and not allow dialysis to define your life.

The definition of Reset means to set, adjust, or fix in a new or different way *(Dictionary.com).* Re-setting, re-adjusting, re-starting, and re-focusing is work and you must do it as many times as needed to achieve a quality level of life while on dialysis. You must also have faith to believe that you can live a quality level of life while on dialysis and stay committed in pursuing progress in every area of your life because you will have your challenges.

Every day I "Reset," my mind from the day before. I tell myself, ***"I am more than what I have been through or going through right now,"*** and I seize the day by maximizing every opportunity I encounter.

Having, The Power to Reset doesn't mean that I do not miss opportunities or totally blow it at times, but it does give the power to prevent being a prisoner of yesterday's failures, disappointments, and losses. Reset gives you the mind of a winner and causes you to never lose because winners win. "Reset" says ***"I don't lose, I learn,"*** and learning is winning.

I learn from yesterday's loses and mistakes. I let go of every bad decision. Then, I "Reset," start over with new ideas, new information, new insight, new stamina, and a new approach to accomplish my goals. Sometimes, I must "Reset," through-out the day to keep my focus and discipline because of the strenuousness of the day.

The Power to Reset renews the strength to continue to believe in hopes, dreams, and desires. Also, it gives the assurance that they do come true. So, expect the next chapters of your life to be the greatest chapters, knowing that dialysis is not your life.

Chapter 8

"The Epilogue"

"I want to inspirit people. I want someone to look at me and say, "I didn't give up because of you"."**-** Fred Hill

I believe it is our purpose to make the best life out of whatever situation life brings. Even while on dialysis, there are newer and richer experiences waiting to be lived. Each new experience is another chapter.- Life has many different chapters and each one is what you make of it. One bad chapter in life does not mean it is the end of the book. If the chapter you are living in now is not great, continue to live it out, knowing that the next one is coming and every chapter in your life has the potential to be amazing. The decisions you make in the chapter you are living in now, can improve the next chapters of your life.

The chapters in my life have been a roller-coaster ride of ups and downs, good and bad, success and failures. What I discovered was that ***life is 10% what happens to you and 90% how you react to it***. I could not give up in the bad times. I could not quit when it got hard. I ***had*** to remain positive and determined to fight for better health to have a better life. We all have a fighter in us, and ***life starts when you discover what you want to fight for.*** I fought for my hopes and dreams. I fought for my wife, son, and family. I fought for my health. I fought for my life.

On February 7, 2015, my fight on dialysis ended and I entered a new chapter in life with a kidney transplant. I continue to live by the same principles of living life to the fullest. I could not take for granted the second chance I had to live without the struggle and pain of being on dialysis.

I realized my life had even a greater purpose because the experience of dialysis caused me to truly appreciate and value my health, my relationship with my wife and son, and life itself and all it had to offer. Most of all, I realized the sacrifice that was made for me to live without dialysis.

My new chance at life through a kidney transplant arose after someone else's death and a family choice to make a gift. I could not take the tragedy of his (or her) death for granted. His (or her) life had to continue to have purpose through me. I had to find a way to live my life louder.

I decided to find a way to make a difference and give back to the kidney community. I never dreamed that a non-profit renal failure fitness program (Better Health Fitness and Motivation) and a book (*Dialysis Is Not Your Life*) would be birthed from the lowest point in my life. I never saw that chapter coming, but through fighting for a better life with renal failure, I'm now living that chapter and excited for the new chapters that will be created. There is still more to come. Stay tuned.

Dialysis Is Not Your Life

ABOUT THE AUTHOR:

Fred Hill is a pastor, teacher, author, personal trainer, and motivator. He is the founder of New Image Church in Spartanburg South Carolina and the author of *"Take Me To The Water."* In 2017 he founded Better Health Fitness & Motivation, a non-profit to help patients with renal failure establish better health through fitness (for the body) and motivation (for the mind and spirit). He is married with one child.

His experience with End Stage Renal Failure (ESRF) inspired him to help bridge the communication gap between the nephrologist and the patient. His passion is to build a community to support those affected by Chronic Kidney Disease (CKD) or Renal Replacement Therapy (RRT).

Other Books by Fred Hill

- **Take Me to The Water**
- **The Power to Reset (Coming Soon)**
- **Journey To Better (Coming Soon)**

Follow me on Instagram:
@Dialysis Is Not Your Life
@realfredhill

www.dialysisisnotyourlife.com
www.betterhealth-fitness.org
www.newimagemin.org

Facebook:
@Dialysis Is Not Your Life

Subscribe to: "Dialysis Is Not Your Life" YouTube channel.

Reference Quotes

1. T.D. Jakes
2. Tony Robbins
3. Dr. Martin Luther King
4. John C. Maxwell
5. Pablo Picasso
6. Nike
7. Eleanor Roosevelt
8. Katherine Hepburn
9. Muhammad Ali

Notes:

Notes:

Notes:

Notes:

Notes:

Notes:

Notes:

Notes:

Made in United States
Troutdale, OR
10/01/2024